Film Tunes

PLAYALONG!

FOR ALTO SAX

Ten top film favourites in melody line arrangements
by Barrie Carson Turner

Chester Music
8/9 Frith Street London W1D 3JB

This book © Copyright 2001 Chester Music
ISBN 0-7119-8320-8
Order No. CH61770
Music processed by Enigma Music
Cover design by Chloë Alexander
Printed in the United Kingdom

Practice points

Each book in the *Applause* series includes suggestions – 'practice points' – on the practice and performance of the pieces in the book.

Each piece has its own list of practice points and exercises to help you in your study of the music. All the exercises, unless we tell you otherwise, follow a set routine. The music is first played for you by our soloist, and then you repeat the music a second and a third time. Metronome clicks introduce each exercise and continue throughout the music, without a break, for all three repetitions, to help you maintain the beat. Where helpful, the exercises are slower than the music on the recording.

We hope you will find the practice points useful.

1 Colors Of The Wind

• This piece is useful for practising your tenuto, legato playing and breath control. Hold the long notes for their full value.

Exercise 1 (CD Track 21)

Bars 4 – 12 set the legato pattern for the whole piece. Listen as we play first, then you repeat the music twice, which begins after four crotchet clicks.
• Be sure to count bar 4 accurately so as not to miss your solo entry on the final quaver.
• Notice that bars 31 – 45 and 47 – 57 are repeats of earlier music. Knowing where the same music is repeated is very useful: you can then avoid practising it twice.

Exercise 2 (CD Track 22)

Exercise 2 uses bars 71 – 75 from the closing section of the piece. In bar 73 it is important to follow the band track carefully so as to judge the speed of the *rit*. Notice bar 74 is *a tempo*. Listen first as we play bars 71 – 75 together with the band track, then you repeat the music twice.
• Play this piece gently, and with feeling.

2 When You Say Nothing At All

• Notice the quaver rest which begins the solo parts at the beginning of bar 5. Many phrases of this song begin like this.

Exercise 1 (CD Track 23)

Exercise 1 repeats bars 5 – 7 three times. We will play the first time, you play the second and third times. Don't play in the rests. The music begins after four crotchet clicks.

Exercise 2 (CD Track 24)

Don't miss the change of time to 2/4 which you briefly meet in bar 16. Exercise 2, bars 13 – 18 includes this bar. The music begins after four crotchet clicks.
• Don't miss the brief change of key between bars 57 – 64.
• Notice the *rit.* In bar 75.

3 Goldfinger

• This song is usually sung in a seductive fashion. Try and imitate this effect by smooth legato playing.
• Stress the dotted minim at the beginning of bar 24. Enjoy this jazz-influenced harmony, made up of the clash between the major and minor 3rds of the chord.

Exercise 1 (CD Track 25)

Exercise 1 introduces you to crotchet triplets, of which there are many in this song. The music, made up of bars 5 – 11, begins with four crotchet clicks. We will play the first time, you repeat the exercise a further two times.

Exercise 2 (CD Track 26)

Exercise 2, made up of bars 20 – 24, also contains crotchet triplets. You will hear seven introductory crotchet clicks before you start. The quaver upbeats come on the eighth click.
• The last three notes of the song should bring the music to a powerful conclusion.

4 Theme from E.T.

• Don't be alarmed by the 3/2 time signature of this piece. Simply count as you would count 3/4, but take special care counting the many changes of time signature in the closing bars of the music.
• The exercises for this music are similar. The rhythm of these extracts is straightforward, but the notes are difficult, and include many accidentals.

Exercise 1 (CD Track 27)

Exercise 1 is made up of bars 27 – 28. Listen as we play it first, then you play it a further two times. The beat is slower than in the recording and the music begins after six crotchet clicks.

Exercise 2 (CD Track 28)

Exercise 2 is based on bars 42 – 45. Aim particularly here for accurate intonation. The tempo is again slower than the recording, and the music begins after six crotchet clicks.
• Play the expansive melody of this piece in a broad, sweeping fashion.
• Take extra breaths where needed for the final long note – but try not to make them too obvious.
• Play the cue notes in bars 37 – 39 if you prefer the lower octave.

5 American Pie

• The rhythms are tricky in this song, particularly in the opening section, but don't worry too much here. If you have the original recording, listen to it, and play in the same relaxed style. If you know the words of the song, allow the natural rhythm of the words to guide you.
• There are long sections in this song when the soloist doesn't play. Count these bars accurately.
• There are many tied notes in this song. Practise the music first without the ties. When you are confident with the rhythm, replace the ties.
• The rhythm quaver-crotchet-quaver is a distinctive feature of this piece. Make sure you understand how to play it.

Exercise 1 (CD Track 29)

Exercise 1 is made up of bars 15 – 20 and demonstrates the style of rhythm that you will meet in this song. Listen as we play the music first, then you play it a further two times. The speed is slightly slower than the song. Four crotchet clicks begin. Notice you play on beat 2 of bar 15.

Exercise 2 (CD Track 30)

Bars 54 – 57 make up exercise 2. The rhythm here is again difficult. The speed is slower than the song, and four crotchet clicks begin.

6 Mission Impossible

• The piece is built almost entirely on only two rhythms. The first is syncopated, and forms the backdrop to the piece, but also occurs in the solo part. It looks fairly frightening on paper, but is less so when you hear it. This rhythm first occurs in bars 3 – 5.
• Pay attention to the important accented notes.

Exercise (CD Track 31)

The second rhythm is easier. Look at bars 7 – 14. To begin, there are eight introductory quaver clicks. Do you see that the two semiquavers make up the first click? The music is slower than the recording.

7 Raiders March

• This is a march tune which requires strong rhythmic playing. Ensure the dotted rhythms are crisp.
• The accents reinforcing the syncopated rhythm in bar 20 and similar places are important.

Exercise 1 (CD Track 32)

Bars 20 – 28 make up exercise 1, which contains a fairly difficult tied triplet rhythm. Practise the music first without the ties. The music begins after seven crotchet clicks.

Exercise 2 (CD Track 33)

Exercise 2 includes tied eighth-note rhythms which you will meet frequently in this piece. Notice these two quavers are not dotted. The music begins after seven crotchet clicks. Listen first as we play, then you repeat the music twice.

8 The Heart Asks Pleasure First

• There are some unusual rhythms in this piece, which require careful attention.

Exercise 1 (CD Track 34)

Exercise 1 introduces you to the difficult dotted quaver rhythm which occurs frequently throughout the music. The cue notes above bar 5 show you how the rhythm fits into the rhythmic structure of the bar. We will play the solo part the first time. You play the second and third times. The music begins after four dotted-quaver clicks.
• The dotted quaver rhythm in exercise 1 above is later frequently mixed with the more usual 6/8 rhythm. Take extra care in counting.

Exercise 2 (CD Track 35)

Don't trip over the change to 9/8 time in bar 13. The time change lasts for one bar only.
• Count this piece in dotted crotchets – two counts for each 6/8 bar and three counts for the 9/8 bar. Counting regularly like this helps you to maintain the rhythm of the music.
• The music should be flowing and smooth.

9 When You Believe

• Count the two introductory bars carefully.
• Take care with the triplets which occur several times during the music. The first quaver is missing, replaced by a rest – but this must still be counted as part of the triplet.

Exercise (CD Track 36)

This exercise is made up of the first four bars of the chorus of the song, bars 12 – 15. The rhythms here are fairly difficult. Practise first without the ties. The music begins after four crotchet clicks.
• Notice that bars 23 – 31 are a repeat of 3 – 11. Knowing which music is repeated saves you practice time.
• Don't miss the change of key at bar 32.
• Play the melody of this song with much warmth, and a full legato.

10 Try A Little Tenderness

• The music of this song is fairly slow, but the rhythms are often difficult, and there are many tied notes. First try playing the music without the ties; then add the ties when you have a more secure grasp of the rhythm. Remember that counting the beat is very important, especially where there are demanding rhythms.

Exercise 1 (CD Track 37)

Bars 7 – 8 make up exercise 1. The music begins with six quaver clicks, then bars 7 – 8 are repeated three times without a break. We will play the first time, you play the second and third times.
• The opening melody of the song is in 6/8 time. Count six as you play, beginning on count three. On the recording you will hear the percussion marking out the beat in bars 5 – 6.

Exercise 2 (CD Track 38)

In bar 23 the music moves into 4/4 time, and the tempo changes. Listen for the percussion marking the new crotchet beats in bar 23. This is quite a tricky moment for you as a soloist, especially as you begin playing on a syncopated note. Count *1 and 2 and 3 and 4 and* for each bar. Counting like this, you play on *and 4 and*. Exercise 2 will help you make the above tempo and time change. Play along with the band track. Bars 21 – 24 are repeated three times without a break. Listen as we play the first time, you play the second and third times. Don't forget to listen for the percussion clicks in the 4/4 section.
• This song has a slow, relaxed blues-jazz feel about it. When you can play the music confidently, try relaxing the rhythm of the melody and create your own jazz feel to the piece.

Colors Of The Wind
(*from* Walt Disney Pictures' "Pocahontas")

Words by Stephen Schwartz
Music by Alan Menken

When You Say Nothing At All
(*from* "Notting Hill")

Words & Music by Paul Overstreet & Don Schlitz

11

Goldfinger
(*from* "Goldfinger")

Words by Leslie Bricusse & Anthony Newley
Music by John Barry

Theme From E.T.
(The Extra-Terrestrial)

Music by John Williams

American Pie
(*from* "The Next Best Thing")

Words & Music by Don McLean

Mission Impossible Theme
(*from* "Mission: Impossible")

Music by Lalo Schifrin

Moderately, heavy beat

Raiders March
(*from* "Raiders Of The Lost Ark")

Music by John Williams

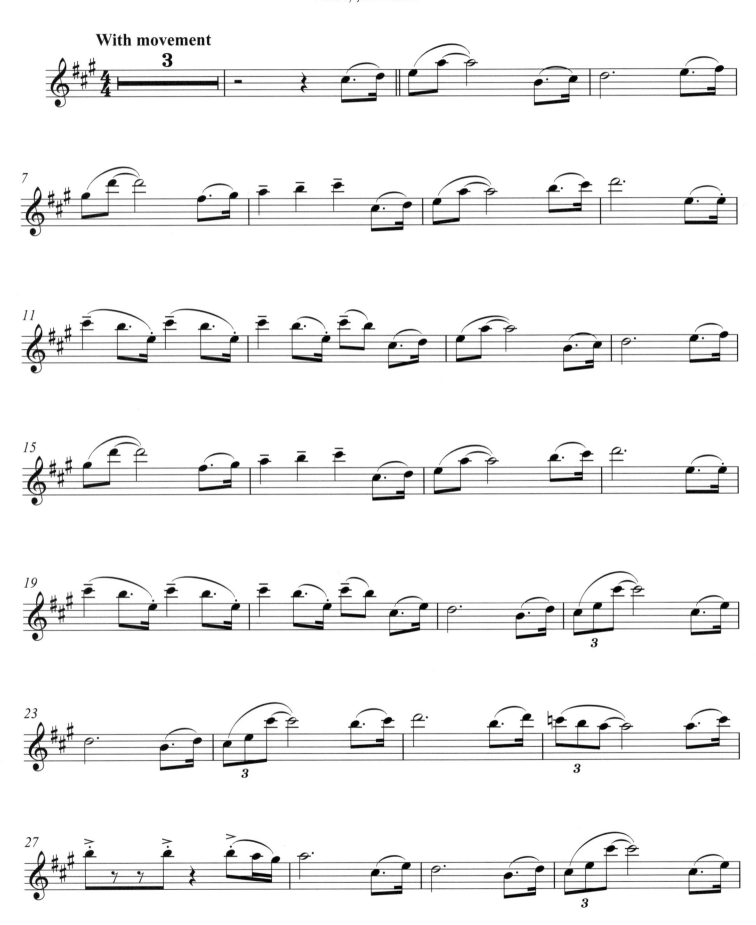

The Heart Asks Pleasure First
(*from* "The Piano")

Music by Michael Nyman

Moderate tempo, flowing

When You Believe
(*from* "The Prince Of Egypt")

Words & Music by Stephen Schwartz
Additional Music by Babyface

Try A Little Tenderness
(*from* "The Commitments")

Words & Music by Harry Woods, Jimmy Campbell & Reg Connelly

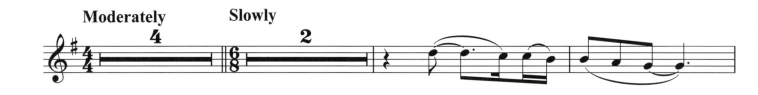

04/03 (47332)